y years.
nd have
Please return/renew this item by the last date shown   families
on this label, or on your self-service receipt.   I have

To renew this item, visit **www.librarieswest.org.uk**   ing and
or contact your library   erience.

Your borrower number and PIN are required.   ings, in
                                                ing this

   it useful

4 6 0239514 8

Who Cares?
Useful information, theories and case studies to help those caring for older relatives or friends.

Sheila Lally

Who Cares?
Useful information, theories and case studies to help those caring for older relatives or friends.

Olympia Publishers
London

www.olympiapublishers.com
OLYMPIA PAPERBACK EDITION

A CIP catalogue record for this title is
available from the British Library.

ISBN: 978-1-80074-049-5

First Published in 2021

Olympia Publishers
Tallis House
2 Tallis Street
London
EC4Y 0AB

Printed in Great Britain

Dedication

For Mum

"To care for those who once cared for us is one of the highest honors" – Tia Walker.

Acknowledgements

I would like to thank my family for their encouragement and particularly my sister, Carmel Golden, for her ongoing support and for proofreading and copy editing the first draft of this book.

A big thank you must also go to the families who have contributed to the case studies either directly or indirectly.

Chapter 1

"Life's challenges are not supposed to paralyze you; they're supposed to help you discover who you are." – *Bernice Johnson Reagon.*

Most countries, due to better health care, have an ageing population as life expectancy increases. In the UK life expectancy at birth is 79 years for males and 83 years for females (Office for National Statistics Sept 2019). The United Nations estimates the global average life expectancy is 73 years. But this should not be seen as a problem. Older people can greatly enhance any society and remain active within their communities. However, as we age, the likelihood is that we will at some point need care by either a professional or family caregiver.

Ageing is a process and not a state and presents opportunities for growth and new experiences. Each age group faces its own set of unique cognitive, psychological, social and emotional set of problems, issues and solutions. No matter what age, vulnerability still exits. Psychologist Eric Erikson (1950) presents a model of human development titled, 'Eight Ages of Man'. Erikson described each stage as a struggle between two emotional opposites, which individuals need to grapple with as part of their development. Erikson's theory has been influential in understanding human development and the development of self-identity.

Eric Erikson's Eight Stages of Development

Age	Psychosocial struggle	Resolution or 'Virtue'	Culmination in old age
Stage One Infancy (0-1 year)	Trust vs Mistrust	Hope	Appreciation of inter-dependence and family connection.
Stage Two Early childhood (1-3 years)	Autonomy vs Doubt	Will	Acceptance of the cycle of life: from the beginning to decline.
Stage Three Pre-school age (3-6 years)	Imitative vs Inadequacy	Purpose	Humour, empathy, resilience.
Stage Four School age (6-12)	Industry vs Inferiority	Competence	Humility: acceptance of the course of one's life and unfulfilled hopes.
Stage Five Adolescence (12-19)	Identity vs Role Confusion	Fidelity	A sense of the complexity of life.
Stage Six Early adulthood (19-25)	Intimacy vs Isolation	Love	A sense of the complexity of relationships: the value of tenderness and loving freely.

Stage Seven Adulthood (25-64)	Generativity vs Self-absorption	Care	Caring for others, empathy and concern.
Stage Eight Old age (65-death)	Integrity vs Despair	Wisdom	A sense of integrity strong enough to withstand physical decline.

The three stages that relate to adults are presented in more detail.

- **Stage Six: Intimacy versus isolation.** The person is a young adult. In this stage, the adult seeks to establish close meaningful relationships. The relationships do not have to be sexual; the important aspect is that there is a mutual emotional bond. If the adult does not establish relationships that have this closeness, the person will have a sense of isolation.

- **Stage Seven: Generativity versus self-absorption.** Middle age. In this stage, the person will show an interest in the world beyond their immediate family. They will be motivated by a concern for society, the environment and future generations. If a person does not cultivate this outlook, they will become self-absorbed and primarily concerned for their material aspirations or pursuit of happiness.

- **Stage eight: Integrity versus despair.** The person is an older adult. The person has time for reflection and as they look back on their life, they may have a sense of satisfaction, this will lead to a feeling of integrity. If the person's reflections result in them feeling they missed key opportunities, then there is an increased risk of experiencing despair. This is partly generated by the sense that it is too late to change anything.

Erikson's model of development proposes that individuals continue to develop throughout their entire lifespan (see box 1 for a case study). Each stage of development centres on the individual's interaction with the social world. The case study presented in box 1 is an example of how an older person has difficulties in the eighth stage of development, i.e. integrity versus despair. Their reflections on their past life, rather than give them a sense of satisfaction, which will lead to a feeling of integrity, has instead generated feelings of despair, perhaps from feelings of opportunities missed and it now being too late to change anything. What could have helped in this situation will be discussed in chapter 5.

Box 1 – Case Study

Vera was a 90-year-old woman whom many would see as having an idyllic childhood being brought up in rural Ireland. She was the youngest of seven children and had two older, adoring brothers.

 In her early twenties, she married and had children of her own and her life revolved around being a housewife and mother. During this time, she also moved to England with her husband and children. It was a challenging and exciting time for Vera and a period of great transition and adaption. Bringing up a family of eight children was not always easy and finances were often tight, despite her efforts to

---

contribute by working part-time. Working outside the home was a positive experience for Vera because mixing with other women of her age group helped with her adaption into a new country.

In middle age, Vera's husband died following a brief illness. She still had a fifteen-year-old son living at home and this gave her a sense of purpose. She continued to work and socialise through her church and had some close friends. Religion was a big part of Vera's life because it offered a supportive community for her.

Vera had always been a very independent woman and found it difficult, as she got older, to accept her increasing loss of mobility. She had good family support: daughters calling on her every day offering to take her out or sit and have a chat. But Vera would often display anger towards her family for no apparent reason and often refused the help and support that was arranged to help her. Her family understood that it was her way of coping with her situation.

Vera became depressed and did not want to engage in social activities that she had once enjoyed; she even stopped going to her local church. She was treated with anti-depressants by her GP, with little effect. She became very reflective and began looking back over her life. She often said she had an unhappy life and appeared troubled by her past, although there was no obvious reason for this. Her family felt her religion would be a comfort to her in these her later years, but this did not seem the case. Vera also became very fearful of dying, which again was surprising for someone with a strong religious belief.

Despite all her family's efforts, Vera's later life was a day-to-day struggle with low mood and feelings of despair.

Adults not only cope with biological and social changes: they also experience physical changes, and many people, as they get older, find the decline in mobility difficult to cope with; this may be due to arthritis, coronary heart disease or circulatory problems, such as a stroke. Other age-related physical changes include a decline in vision, hearing and information processing. The decline in information processing is accelerated in cases of dementia and Alzheimer's disease, which is discussed in more detail in chapter 7.

Chapter 2

"Sometimes asking for help is the most meaningful example of self-reliance." - from the poem 'Sometimes' by *US Senator Cory Booker.*

As we age so may our need for additional care and support. Most people will want to stay in their own homes for as long as possible and this may be achieved with some help. Often the older person's needs may be straightforward. In many cases, having the right information or taking simple, practical measures will keep people living in their own home with the level of independence they want for much longer. In most areas, there will be community and voluntary organisations that may be able to help. A useful starting point to find out what services are available in your area is your local library. Some services may also be advertised at your GP surgery or in other community settings. These include things like pop-in sessions for coffee and a chat at local community settings to lunch clubs where a hot meal and the opportunity for some social time can be found.

Age UK is a very useful resource because they provide a range of services to support older people living at home. They provide free information and advice to help on topics as diverse as claiming benefits to finding a care home, these include:

- **Money and Legal**: help with benefits, managing money, avoiding scams and legal matters.
- **Health and Wellbeing**: get information on age-related health conditions, tips and advice on staying fit and healthy, as well as information to help navigate a way through the often complex health service processes, including hospital discharge planning.
- **Care and Support**: help to get the right care. Arranging social care can be a challenge: from knowing where to start to what type of care and support is needed, and who pays for it.
- **Work and Learning**: help and information to stay in employment or find a new job. Computer training is provided to help improve IT skills.
- **Travel and Hobbies**: you are never too old to enjoy a favourite hobby or to begin a new one. Helpful information is also provided about continuing to drive safely.

An older person, or their family, can self-refer to Age UK. Some areas will have an outlet that will help with queries and take referrals. Alternatively, they have a very user-friendly website: www.ageuk.org.uk

The British Red Cross also provides support and care to help older people to live independently at home. They provide support following a stay in hospital and they make sure the older person has everything they need for the first 24 to 72 hours when they are back at home. Depending on the level of need, the Red Cross may then provide help for 12 weeks. Other possible support, depending on the area, includes:

- transport home from hospital,
- door-to-door transport for essential health-care

appointments,
- help with everyday tasks,
- companionship,
- rebuilding confidence,
- help to arrange for bills to be paid,
- short-term use of a wheelchair and toilet aids.

Referrals to the Red Cross are often made by the hospital where the older person is an inpatient, or often the GP will make a referral. However, self-referrals can also be made. They also have a very user-friendly website: www.redcross.org.uk/get-help/get-support-at-home

Increasing Care Needs

If the older person is finding it difficult to manage at home, they may be considering arranging for a care and support provider to help with personal tasks such as washing and dressing, getting in and out of bed or staying safe within their home. These can be met either by buying the support needed directly from a provider or requesting an assessment by their local council. If you have a provider in mind, you can approach them directly and request that they carry out an assessment. If you need help to find a provider, your local council can provide you with a list or you can look at the Care Quality Commission's website: www.cqc.org.uk/ The Care Quality Commission monitor, inspect and regulate health and social care services; they publish what they find, including ratings to help people choose the right care.

If the older person wishes to have an assessment carried out by their local council (www.gov.uk/find-local-council)

this can be achieved by contacting it by telephone or via their website and looking for Adult Care Services or Social Care. An assessment of needs is free. It consists of a discussion between the older person and a trained person from the council, where the older person can talk about the care and support needs they have and the goals they may want to achieve, i.e. to continue to live independently in their own home.

The box below provides a space to record the contact details of the older person's local council and the name of the allocated social worker.

Local council's contact details
Name of the social worker:

The most well-known theory of needs is that presented by Maslow (1970). Maslow proposes that all humans have a hierarchy of needs. We first need to satisfy basic biological needs, such as food, warmth, etc. We will then be pulled to meet higher needs. See Maslow's Pyramid of Needs below.

Maslow proposed that each level of needs is a powerful motivating force for individuals. At first, we are preoccupied with meeting our biological needs. If our need for food, water and warmth is not being met then all the other 'higher' needs become unimportant. We must satisfy our biological needs first. Once our biological needs are fully met, we will have an increased desire to have our need for safety and security met. This may include physical safety, i.e. free from abuse, but it also means stability, such as social and economic stability. Maslow (see pyramid) termed these as basic needs of individuals. Once these basic needs are met, we are equally as motivated to meet our psychological needs: our need to love and be loved, to have friends and belong to a wider group or community. Once our belonging and love needs are met, the importance of our self-esteem needs is heightened. This need includes being able to achieve tasks, being independent, having a sense of achievement for one's strength and to feel you have respect from others. Once our self-esteem needs are met, we seek to feel self-fulfilled; this may be from an activity you have achieved, such as building a garden shed or knitting a jumper. It may be from a feeling of achievement, such as seeing your children as adults who are contributing to society.

Although Maslow presented his needs theory as a hierarchy or progressive pyramid, he emphasised the fact that individuals did not necessarily work through the stages in a methodical or ordered way. A person could be seeking to meet their needs from two or three stages at the same time. However, an individual would only be motivated to strive for meeting a higher stage once a lower stage was fully or largely satisfied.

Maslow's Pyramid of Needs

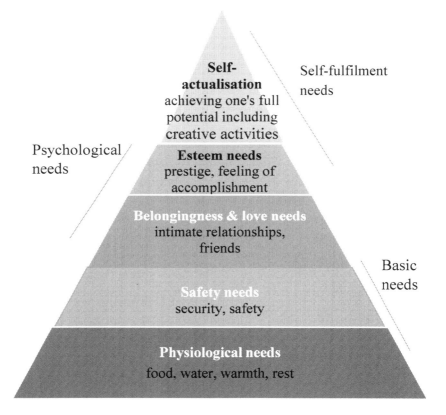

Preparing for the Needs Assessment

Before a Needs Assessment is carried out by the older person's local council, it is worth thinking through Maslow's needs theory and using this as a guide to how **all** the older person's needs are being met, not just their basic care needs, i.e. the first two levels.

All the different aspects of the older person's life will be looked at during the assessment, including any emotional, psychological and physical needs. The person carrying out the assessment will normally be a social worker or social worker assistant. Sometimes you may also want to arrange a separate assessment from an occupational therapist about home adaptions, such as grab rails, stairlifts or ramps, etc. The key is to make sure the older person understands that this is their opportunity to discuss their needs and to contribute to a care plan that realistically meets these needs. The older person can have a relative or friend present during the assessment.

Many older people can downplay their needs and present themselves as more independent than they are. It is important that they are prepared for the assessment and think about how they manage day-to-day activities. They may have good and bad days, but it is only what is presented during the assessment that will be part of the care plan that determines the level of care the older person is entitled to. So, they need to be realistic about how they manage on the bad days, even if this is something they do not like to admit.

Notes/Questions you would like to ask

During the assessment

Be prepared for the assessment to take about an hour, because all aspects of the older person's life will be discussed, including emotional, psychological and physical care needs. The older person will be asked questions relating to their medical history and needs. Here is a selection of questions they might be asked:
- What medical problems do you currently have or have had in the past?
- What medication do you take?
- Do you have any ongoing health problems, such as arthritis, circulatory problems or heart problems?

An assessment of how the older person manages day-to-day tasks will be carried out. An 'activities of daily living approach' is usually used. This is how individuals manage everyday tasks such as described in table 1.

Table 1 – Activities of daily living

Activity of living	What might affect this?
Bathing and showering	Can the older person do this safely?
Personal hygiene and grooming	Getting dressed, which includes being able to select clothes appropriate for the weather conditions. Brushing/combing hair.
Functional mobility: often referred to as how an older person can 'transfer'	Can they get in and out of a chair or in and out of bed?

Continence management	Are they able to use the bathroom to maintain continence, e.g. can they get there in time and manage to pull underwear up and down? If continence aids such as pads are used, can they change these when necessary?
Mobility	How does the older person get around? Can they use the stairs, if that is applicable? Can they safely get around the house?
Feeding	Can the older person feed themself? Not necessarily a meal they have prepared themself.
Cleaning and maintaining the house	Can the older person clean the toilet, for example, do their laundry and keep the house reasonably tidy?
Managing money	Can they manage to pay their bills, manage their pension and other benefits?
Preparing meals	Planning and preparing a range of nutritious meals, not just simple things like soup and bread.
Shopping for groceries and necessities	This includes picking up any medication that is needed.
Managing medications	Are they safely able to take medication? Do they have the dexterity to open bottles, etc.?
Communication and social life	Using the telephone. Getting out and about and engaging with their local community, i.e. keeping in touch with friends and maintaining hobbies.

Since 2014, there has been a national level framework of care and support needs that all councils will consider when assessing what help they can give individuals. The council will assess an individual's care and support needs, as outlined above, and decide if they meet the eligibility criteria set out in the Community Care Act (2014). The older person's needs could be eligible if they are not able to do a combination of certain things that seriously affect their wellbeing. This may include washing, getting dressed, getting in and out of bed or keeping their home safe to live in.

To meet the Care Act's eligibility criteria, a person's needs must meet the three following conditions:

1. They have care and support needs as a result of a physical or mental impairment or illness.
2. Because of those needs, they cannot achieve two or more of the outcomes specified below.
3. As a consequence of being unable to achieve these outcomes, there is, or there is likely to be, a significant impact on the older person.

Outcomes:

- to carry out basic self-care activities as part of normal daily life, such as eating, drinking, toileting, dressing, etc.,
- maintaining a habitable home environment,
- being able to make use of the home safely,
- to maintain family and other significant personal relationships and with a focus on these relationships, which if not maintained would significantly impact on a person's wellbeing,

- to access and engage in work, training, education and volunteering,
- to access the facilities and services in the community, including recreational opportunities important to the individual.

Following the Needs Assessment

Following the assessment, the assessor will usually give some indication if the older person is eligible for care and support. If they are eligible, then a discussion will take place as to how their needs may be met. This will be based solely on the information that was given during the assessment.

If the older person does not have eligible needs, they will be given information and advice about what care and support are available locally to help. This could be help from local charities or voluntary organisations, for example. The council may also offer to refer the older person to other organisations who can support the older person's wellbeing and help them to remain independent for longer.

Financial Assessment

If the older person is eligible for care and support from the council, they may have to pay something towards the cost. To find out how much they might need to pay, the council will ask to do a financial means test or a financial assessment, and the older person would need to disclose details about their savings, assets and income. This assessment can also be helpful to ensure the older person is claiming all the benefits they are entitled to, and at the correct level, i.e. Attendance Allowance, Pension Credit, etc. This will be discussed in more detail in chapter 4.

Box 2 – Case Study

Anna has been helping to look after her mother (Pearl), who is becoming increasingly less mobile and struggling to do day-to-day tasks, such as getting out of bed in the morning, getting dressed and preparing breakfast. Anna works full-time and does not live that close to her mother; she does not know where to turn to get extra help. Pearl currently has a private carer who comes to help three days a week for an hour, which Anna pays for. The carer helps to get Pearl out of bed, makes her breakfast and does a little light housework.

Anna cannot afford to pay privately for any more help and feels desperate to find a way forward to get extra help for her mother. A friend suggested that she approach the local council and request a Needs Assessment. Anna spoke to an adviser on the Adult Care Help Desk at the council, whom she found to be very helpful. She gave Anna advice and support and also indicated how long she would have to wait for the assessment; because it was not deemed an emergency, it could take up to six weeks. However, the Needs Assessment was arranged within three weeks.

Before the Needs Assessment by a social worker, an occupational therapy assistant arranged to call on Pearl and asked if Anna would like to be present. This assessment focused on how Pearl was managing to get around the house, get on and off the toilet, use the stairs and get in and out of the house. As a result of this assessment, Pearl was given some techniques that she could use to help herself when getting in and out of her chair and toilet. The

---

occupational therapy assistant also suggested several adaptions to help keep Pearl independent and safe within her own home; these included a raised toilet seat, a seat to sit on whilst in the shower and blocks to raise Pearl's armchair. Pearl already had a stairlift fitted, which she funded herself. Grab rails would be fitted by the front door to make it easier for Pearl to manage to get up and down the step, so enabling her to get out of the house. These simple adaptions and advice made a big difference to Pearl and would enable her to be more independent within her own home. As a result, Anna felt she was safer from falls.

Anna and Pearl prepared for the Needs Assessment by thinking through how Pearl managed day-to-day activities and how Pearl managed on a 'bad day'. During the assessment, the social worker discussed Pearl's physical needs as well as her mental and emotional needs. The outcome of the assessment, and the plan of care that Pearl and Anna agreed, was that Pearl would have a carer provided by the council for the four mornings she currently did not have any support. This would help Pearl to get up, washed (including a shower, as needed) and to prepare her breakfast. Pearl stated she did not want help to get into bed at night, because she felt she was able to manage this herself. Likewise, she did not want community meals delivered because she was able to order, and have delivered, frozen meals that she could heat in the microwave. Pearl was offered social activities to attend within the community, such as a lunch club, but she declined these because she felt well supported in her social and emotional needs by her family and friends.

Anna had expressed her concerns about her mother living alone and her risk of falls. In response to this, the social worker discussed 'Telecare' or technology-enabled care, which is a range of simple wireless sensors and alarms designed to help people live safely and independently in their homes. The social worker explained that it would involve Pearl wearing a pendant or wrist band, which when pressed would trigger a call to a call centre that operates 24 hours a day, 7 days a week. The call centre operator will immediately know who is calling because this information would be provided to the company when the system was set up. The operator will attempt to speak to Pearl and offer verbal help or send appropriate help to her home. A list of family and neighbours who can respond in an emergency will have been provided, and if they cannot be contacted, then someone from the council would be sent to help. Both Pearl and Anna agreed that they wanted to be referred for this service; the social worker stated that there would be a one-off installation charge, then a weekly charge.

The social worker also asked about Pearl's benefits and financial situation; Pearl appeared to be getting all the benefits she was entitled to.

Pearl and Anna felt happy with the meeting and the care plan that was agreed. The social worker said that a written copy of the care plan would be sent to Pearl and the care provider who would be supporting Pearl on the four mornings. The council would also calculate what Pearl's contribution would be for her care package and provide a written statement.

Chapter 3

"There are only four kinds of people in the world. Those who have been caregivers. Those who are currently caregivers. Those who will be caregivers, and those who will need a caregiver." – *Rosalyn Carter.*

Sometimes even with substantial adaptions to the older person's home, such as installing a stairlift or downstairs toilet, it may be necessary to consider moving into a more protective environment. Sheltered housing and extra care housing (also called retirement housing) is designed specifically with the needs of older people in mind. It can help keep the older person's independence, whilst making sure help is available when they need it.

Sheltered housing

In sheltered housing, the older person's home will be designed to make it easier for them to live there independently. Usually, these will include lifts, ramps for wheelchairs and grab rails.

There will be a person who looks after the building, i.e. a scheme manager or 'warden', but they may not be on site. Most sheltered housing schemes will have a system for how often the scheme manager will contact residents, depending on need. However, there is always 24-hour emergency help available through an alarm system, i.e. emergency pull cords are located in each room. Independent/external care workers can still be used to provide help with personal care needs.

Sheltered housing usually provides some shared facilities, e.g. laundry service and a communal lounge. This type of accommodation is best if the older person can live independently but is looking for a more manageable home, with help available in an emergency. If the older person needs more support or care, then it may be worth considering extra care housing.

Extra care housing

Extra care housing is similar to sheltered housing, but the older person will be able to get help with personal care from care workers based at the complex. This could include washing, dressing, eating and some household tasks. The older person will still be living independently but with the reassurance that there are staff on-site or on-call 24 hours a day. Like sheltered housing, there are usually some shared facilities and there is often a communal dining room.

Moving into residential housing can delay or prevent a move to a care home because it has the facilities to offer 24-hour help in an emergency. However, if the older person is likely to need more care in the future than can be offered by a residential housing scheme, and will need to move into a care home, they need to think about whether they would be happy to move again.

Retirement housing schemes are run by councils, housing associations, charities or private companies. A good place to start, if you are unsure whether retirement housing would be suitable for the person you care for or would like to know how to get into such a scheme, is to request a Needs Assessment from the local council. The process for this has been outlined in chapter 2. If the Needs Assessment identifies that retirement housing is needed, a social worker will give information to help choose an appropriate scheme to meet the older person's needs. The assessment may indicate that the older person needs more support than can be met in a retirement housing scheme and a care home will be needed.

Care homes

Care homes provide residential care if substantial support is needed with personal care. Personal care refers to help to look after your physical needs, such as help with washing, dressing and going to the toilet.

There are different types of care home settings, depending on the type of care that is needed:

- residential care homes (personal care),
- nursing homes (personal care with nursing care),
- care homes with dementia care.

Residential care homes offer 24-hour help with personal care, such as washing, dressing, getting to the toilet, eating and drinking and taking medication. Nursing care is not included.

Nursing care homes offer all the support that a care home would, but a registered nurse is on duty at all times. This would be suitable for older people who have complex health needs and need regular attention from a nurse.

Care homes with dementia care offer specialist care for people with dementia. They will have care assistants with dementia experience. A nurse with similar experience may also be available.

Some care homes are 'dual registered' meaning they have residential care rooms as well as nursing care rooms. If the older person's needs are likely to change in the near future, it is a good idea to consider such a care home. This will avoid a move to another home as their care needs increase.

Moving into a care home will require a big adjustment for most people, particularly if it involves moving in a crisis, for example, following a hospital admission. (See the case study in box 3). This move can be viewed as a transition. Transition is a psychological process that individuals go through. Everyone goes through the process of change at their own pace. Some are quicker to let go of the past and more excited about new beginnings. William Bridges presents a model outlining three stages in transitions – see table 2. He proposes that the process itself is the same for everyone, and it is the transitions between each stage that creates discomfort rather than the change itself.

It is clear from the case study in box 3 that it is not only the older person moving into a care home who experiences, and has to navigate, this transition, but families of that person also experience, and have to navigate, the process of personal transitions. Moving into a care home appears to be a parallel transition process for the older person and also for their family. This will be discussed further in chapter 7.

Table 2

Stages in Transition by William Bridges

Ending	Neutral Zone	New Beginning
Grieving: loss due to change.	Anxiety rises and motivation falls.	Involves new understandings, new values, new ways to think about yourself.
May see overreaction to change.	People may feel overwhelmed, disoriented, self-doubting.	Need to be nurtured like a plant would be.
Acknowledge losses – get them out in the open.	People are divided – some want to move forward, others want to remain the same.	Clarify and communicate the purpose.

Box 3 – Case Study

Pam had been receiving help with personal care every morning; this had been organised following a Needs Assessment by her local council. This had been going well, and Pam was becoming more accepting that she needed this support. She had been very reluctant at the start.

Pam was getting increasingly less mobile and her family were concerned about her living alone. She did have a pendant that she could use in an emergency and a member of her family would respond. She had used this on a few occasions when she had fallen. On one such occasion, Pam had fallen and had injured her leg and was admitted to hospital.

During her hospital stay, Pam had input from the physiotherapist to help with her mobility, and she had an assessment from an occupational therapist. She was also referred to the hospital social worker for an assessment around her home situation, in readiness for discharge. Pam's family felt that Pam was not safe at home because she was falling more frequently and found it difficult getting around the house. Pam agreed to be discharged from hospital to a residential care home for a trial period.

Pam's family looked at care homes they thought would be suitable, using the information given to them by the social worker and available on the Care Quality Commission website. They arranged for Pam to visit the one they considered the most suitable. During the visit, Pam was shown around the home and introduced to the staff. The care manager carried out a brief assessment of Pam's needs and felt that the care home would be able to meet her needs. Pam agreed to move in for a trial period of six weeks until she felt stronger and more able to cope in her own home.

Before the move, Pam's family personalised Pam's room at the care home by bringing in things from Pam's home: photos, cushions, rugs, etc.

At first, Pam was anxious and fearful about the move but happy that she was out of hospital. But soon she became angry and threatened to leave the care home. Pam's family, on advice from the care manager, played down her threat to leave and said she should give it a chance. Everyone chivvied Pam along saying it was best, at this time, for her to be in a more protected environment. But Pam put more and more demands on her family to take her home. Different options were put to Pam, e.g. she could stay with her daughter for a while, but Pam insisted on going back to her own house. The care home manager advised to give it a bit longer to see if Pam would settle.

During this time, Pam appeared to be depressed and her family felt guilty for putting their mother through this. They were struggling to cope with Pam's wishes because they were concerned for her safety living alone. Pam's daughter decided to contact the local council and request another Needs Assessment, with an option of putting in a care package that would enable Pam to return to her own home. The social worker agreed to visit Pam in the care home to do the assessment. A care package to support Pam in her own home was agreed, but due to re-organisation within the council's care provision, it would take some time to implement. Pam was frustrated and a bit hostile but accepted this when her daughter said that she could return home but not yet because there was no help available to support her.

As time went on, Pam started to gradually accept living in the care home and started to join in some of the activities. Her family continued to visit regularly and take her out and about. When an appropriate care provider was eventually commissioned by the council to deliver the care package that would mean Pam could go home, Pam had doubts about going home because she felt she would struggle to get around her house and look after herself, even with carers coming in twice a day. Her daughter gave Pam time to make her decision and told her it was her choice to make.

In the end, Pam decided to stay in the care home because she felt safer in this protected environment.

Chapter 4

"Never underestimate your problem or your ability to deal with it." - *Robert H. Schuller*.

The number of people paying for their care is growing. Whilst some people will qualify for funding from their council, many will end up paying for all their care themselves. A person who is paying for their care, rather than getting financial help from their local council, is often referred to as self-funding. As discussed in chapter 2, the best place to start, if more help is needed by an older person, is a Needs Assessment. The local council has a statutory obligation to carry out a Needs Assessment if care and support appear to be needed. This is regardless of the older person's finances or whether they may qualify for help; the Needs Assessment is free.

After the Needs Assessment, a financial assessment will be carried out to determine whether the council should pay for any of the older person's care; this may be for care in their own home or for care in a care home. The assessment is not as daunting as it sounds; it's basically a series of questions related to the older person's income and savings. It will also help to ensure the older person is getting the benefits they are entitled to, and at the correct level.

Table 3 - Savings limits for care at home or within a care home (2020 rate shown, subject to change)

The older person has over £23,250 in savings/investments or a weekly income more than the care fees.	The older person will have to pay for all their care.
The older person has between £14,250 and £23,250 in savings/investments.	Savings between these amounts will be calculated as providing an income of £1 a week for every £250 of savings. The older person will also have to contribute from their income, i.e. pensions and benefits.
The older person has under £14,250 in savings/investments.	The older person will not have to use this towards their care costs, but they will have to contribute from their income, i.e. pensions and benefits.

(Adapted from *Paying for your care* produced by Independent Age)

Care at home: Following the financial assessment, the council will provide the older person with a statement outlining their contribution that will need to be paid towards their care. The value of their property is not included as savings/investments – as shown in table 3 – so the older person will not have to sell their property to fund care at home. If an older person is assessed as needing short-term care to enable them to 'get back on their feet', i.e. following a stay in hospital, the council should provide free care for approx. 6 weeks, enabling the older person to regain their independence at home.

Care in a care home: If the older person owns their own home, its value will be included when calculating their capital/investments. Moving into a care home is a difficult time for any older person and their family, as discussed in chapter 3. For this reason, if the older person has less than £23,250 in savings, apart from the value of their house, the council will not include the value of their house in its calculation of their savings/investments for the first 12 weeks following a permanent move to a care home. This is to give them time to sell their house or consider other options. The value of an older person's home will not be included when calculating savings/investments if it will still be the main home of:

- the older person's partner or former partner,
- a close relative who is 60 or over,
- a close relative who is incapacitated (for example, eligible for disability benefits such as Attendance Allowance).

See the case study in box 4 for an example of a financial assessment.

Box 4 – Case Study

Bill was struggling to manage to look after himself at home. Although his son, Jason, lived in the same house, Jason was not able to provide Bill with consistent support. Bill was the one who had

---

provided support for Jason over the years. Jason had mental health problems and was not always able to work due to his personality and anxiety disorder. He was receiving benefits to help support himself. Bill's daughter (Sarah) was concerned about her father and spoke to the council and requested a Needs Assessment. A care package was agreed to meet Bill's needs at home. The financial assessment indicated that Bill had over £23,250 in savings, therefore, he would have to contribute towards his care.

After a short period of carers going in to see Bill twice or three times daily, it became clear that more care and support was needed than could be provided within the home. Bill decided his best option was to move into a residential care home. The council provided information and support to help choose a care home that Bill would be happy with. Bill's main concern was what would happen to Jason if the house had to be sold – Bill would have to pay the care home fees because he was assessed as having the means to self-fund.

Bill felt that he should not have to pay for his care and that his house should not be included in the financial assessment. He asked Sarah to help him give away some of his money to his grandchildren and to sign the house over to Jason so that his assets would be below £23,250.

Sarah was also concerned about the implications for her brother if Bill's house had to be sold. But she said to her father that what he was asking was not an appropriate thing to do and could have serious consequences. However, she agreed to speak to the social worker and see if there was anything that could help Jason to stay in the house.

The social worker was very understanding of Bill's concerns about paying for care but told him that the majority of older people will be paying for their care. She told Bill that if in the future his funds are close to (within 3 months) falling below the threshold of £23,250, he should contact the council to request a reassessment of his financial and care needs.

The social worker also considered whether the house should be sold to pay for Bill's care home fees. Because Jason was a close relative and had lived in the house for most of his life, had mental health problems, and was in receipt of a disability benefit, the value of the house would not be included as an asset. Therefore, it would not have to be sold to pay for Bill's care and Jason could continue to live there.

Bill now felt happier about moving into a care home knowing that if his funds got low, the council would step in and help to pay his care home fees. He was also greatly relieved that Jason would not have to move out of the family home.

NHS help to pay for care

In some situations, the NHS may be responsible for paying for the older person's care. This will be the case if the older person has complex medical needs that mainly need health care rather than social care. If they do have a high level of health and care needs, the older person may qualify for NHS continuing healthcare. If they do, the NHS will arrange, and pay, for all the health care the older person is assessed as needing. This could be provided at home or in a care home, usually a nursing home.

NHS funded nursing care is when the NHS pays for the nursing care component of nursing homes' fees. The NHS pays a flat rate (rate in 2021: £183.92 a week) directly to the care home towards the cost of nursing care. To find out whether the older person is eligible they will need to have an NHS continuing healthcare assessment; this is often part of the Needs Assessment carried out by a representative from the council. If they do need an NHS continuing healthcare assessment, one can be arranged by speaking to their GP, social worker or contacting the local Clinical Commissioning Group (CCG).

Topping up care home fees

If the older person's choice of care home accommodation costs more than their local council is willing to pay, someone else can make up the difference between that amount and the home's fees. This is known as third-party top-up fees and is usually paid by a relative, friend or another third party. The older person may choose to live in a more expensive care home to be closer to family or they like the comfort offered in a care home that would not be fully covered by the local council.

Things to consider before agreeing to pay for a relative's top-up fees:

- What would happen if your circumstances changed and you could no longer afford the top-up fee?
- Care home fees often increase every year, but local councils do not always increase their funding at the same rate. Therefore, you could find yourself paying more each year to cover the difference in fees.

Benefits that the older person may be eligible to claim:

Pension Credit is a benefit that gives the older person extra money to top up their pension income (the full basic state pension is currently £179.60 a week – 2021 rate). There are two types of Pension Credit:

1.**Guarantee Credit** tops up the older person's income if it is below a minimum weekly amount set by the government. (The 2021 rate is £177.10 for a single person or £270.30 for a couple.) If the older person qualifies, they will also be entitled to other benefits, such as free NHS dental treatment and help to pay their rent and council tax.

2.**Savings Credit** gives the older person extra money each week if they have saved some money towards their retirement. The older person needs to be over 65 and have reached their state pension age before 6th April 2016 to be eligible to claim it. They could get £14.05 extra for a single person or £15.17 for a couple (rate in 2021/2022).

Attendance Allowance is extra money paid if the older person has a long-term disability or condition, or if they need help with personal support or supervision to keep safe. Personal support includes getting dressed, washing, eating, going to the toilet, getting in and out of bed and taking medication. Supervision means the older person needs someone to watch over them to keep them safe, e.g. prompt them to take their medication or to prevent a fall.

It does not matter whether the older person is currently receiving help with personal support or supervision: it is only a requirement that they need such help.

The older person can claim Attendance Allowance if the following criteria apply:

- has reached state pension age,
- has a long-term disability or condition,
- has needed frequent help for at least six months with personal care or supervision because of their disability.

Attendance Allowance is not means-tested, so the older person's income and savings are not taken into account. There are two weekly rates:

- The lower rate is paid if help is needed either in the day or at night. (The 2021/2022 rate is £60.00 per week.)
- The higher rate is paid if help is needed both during the day and at night. (The 2021/2022 is rate £89.60 per week.)

Receiving Attendance Allowance can entitle the older person to other help, such as a Blue Badge that makes parking closer to shops, etc. much easier. This will help the older person get out and about with a family member or on their own.

Help with Council Tax: Council Tax Support helps people with a low income to pay their council tax. Each council sets its criteria, so the best place to start is by contacting the local council. The older person may qualify if they have a low income. If they are receiving Guarantee Pension Credit, they will also be eligible for Council Tax Support. Full council tax rates are based on at least two people living in a property. If the older person lives alone, they will be entitled to a 25% reduction in council tax. To make sure the discount is applied, let the council know that the older person is living alone. Not everyone is counted for council tax purposes. For example, they will be regarded as living alone if they live with someone:

- who is severely mentally impaired,
- who is a full-time student,
- who is a long-term hospital patient,
- who is a live-in care worker.

If the older person lives with someone who is disregarded for council tax purposes, they will still be eligible to pay council tax, but at a reduced rate.

Box 5 – Case Study

Nania had osteoarthritis in both knees; this affected her mobility. She found it particularly difficult getting out of her chair and getting to the toilet. As a result, she often didn't make it in time and had to wear incontinence pads. She had the same problem at night. Nania was struggling to cope with the increased amount of washing, i.e. her clothes and bedding. She also found keeping her flat clean increasingly difficult.

Her daughter-in-law suggested she may be eligible for Attendance Allowance, and they completed the form together. The form looked daunting at first, but they persevered after getting some advice from the Attendance Allowance helpline (0800 731 0122).

The helpline advised Nania to give as much information as possible about her care needs, even if she felt it was embarrassing or not very relevant. They advised her to state how frequently she needed help, how long it took her to do certain tasks and how much help she needed with them because they look at how much help you need, not how much help you are currently getting. Therefore, it is important to state the help needed even if there isn't anyone to help.

Nania was awarded Attendance Allowance at the lower rate;

---

this meant she was also eligible for Pension Credit, which boosted her income considerably. She also got more help with housing benefit and Council Tax Support. This meant Nania could pay for a cleaner to keep her flat clean and tidy and to help with the laundry and shopping.

At the same time, Nania also applied for a Blue Badge, which she was awarded due to her lack of mobility and difficultly walking distances. This made it so much easier for Nania and her family when they went out. It meant that Nania found going to restaurants and her favourite hobby of bingo so much more accessible. When her family were not available to take her to bingo, Nania was now able to afford a taxi.

Receiving these benefits made a big difference to Nania; she was happy that she did not have to worry about her finances and was able to get the help she needed to stay independent. Having the Blue Badge meant that she could get out and about and keep connected with her community and continue to enjoy her hobby.

Chapter 5

"Some days there won't be a song in your heart. Sing anyway." - *Emory Austin.*

Most of us will feel lonely at some point in our lives. However, older people are especially vulnerable to loneliness and social isolation. This may be due to adult children moving away, friends or partners have died, and health problems may make it harder for them to get out and about to see others.

Hundreds of thousands of older people in the UK are lonely and feel cut off; this is especially true for those over the age of 75. According to Age UK, more than two million people in England over the age of 75 live alone. More than one million older people say they go for over a month without speaking to a friend, neighbour or family member.

Being alone does not always mean you will feel lonely; people often spend time alone and enjoy their own company. Many other people say they feel lonely even when they are surrounded by people. Loneliness is a personal experience, but it usually involves feelings of sadness. Someone who is feeling lonely may also find it difficult to reach out to others. There is a stigma surrounding loneliness, and older people often feel too proud to ask for help. But it is important to remember that loneliness can, and does, affect anyone of any age.

To help overcome these feelings, it often helps to identify when the older person feels lonely. It may be on particular days or particular times of the year. Some people find the weekends a lonely time, because this may have been a time when they previously spent time with their family. Others say that when the clocks change and the days get longer in spring, this can feel a very lonely time. By identifying what can trigger feelings of loneliness, the older person can then put things in place to try and improve how they feel. NHS England (www.nhs.uk/) has suggested the following ways for older people to connect with others and feel useful and appreciated again.

- **Smile, even if it feels difficult:** Take every opportunity to smile at others or begin a conversation: for example, with the check-out operator at the supermarket, or the person sat next to you in the doctor's waiting room. If you feel shy, or not sure what to say, start by asking people about themselves.

- **Invite friends for tea:** If you are feeling down and alone, it is tempting to think nobody wants to visit you, but often friends, family and neighbours will appreciate receiving an invitation to come and spend some time with you. If you would prefer someone else to host the get-together, the charity Contact the Elderly (https://www.contact-the-elderly.org.uk/) holds regular free Sunday afternoon parties for people over the age 75 who live alone. They will be collected from their home and driven to a volunteer host's home for the afternoon.

- **Keep in touch by phone:** Having a chat with a friend or relative over the phone can be the next best thing to being with them. The following organisations have volunteers who provide friendship calls to older people:
  - The Silver Line (https://www.thesilverline.org.uk/what-we-do/ or Tel 0800 4 70 80 90)
  - Independent Age (https://www.independentage.org/ or Tel 0800 319 6789)
  - Age UK (https://www.ageuk.org.uk/information-advice/health-wellbeing/loneliness/ or Tel 0800 055 6112)
  - Friends of the Elderly (https://www.fote.org.uk?service-post=phoning-firends or Tel 0300 332 1119).

- **Learn to love computers:** If your friends and family live far away, a good way to stay in touch, especially with grandchildren, is by using a personal computer or tablet (a handheld computer). You can share emails and photos with family and friends, have free video chats using services such as Skype and FaceTime or Messenger via Facebook. A tablet computer can be especially useful if you cannot get around very easily because you can sit with it on your knee or have it close to hand. Also, the screen is clear and bright. A sponge tip stylus pen or speech recognition may help if the touchscreen is difficult due to arthritic hands or fingers with poor circulation.

Libraries and community centres often hold regular training courses for older people to learn basic computer skills. They are also a good place to meet and spend time with others. Local branches of Age UK (https://www.ageuk.org.uk/no-one/we-enable-independence/) run classes in computing to help older people get to grips with smartphones, tablet computers and email. Get some tips and advice on how to become more confident using the Internet (https://www.nhs.uk/accessibility/become-a-confident-internet-user/) including how to access your GP surgery online and how to look for reliable online health information.

- **Get involved in local community activities:** These will vary according to where you live, but the chances are you will have access to a singing or walking group, book clubs, bridge, bingo, quiz nights or lunch club. Find out about what is going on in your area through your local library, or ask at your GP surgery. The Silver Line helpline (https://www.thesilverline.org.uk/ or Tel 0800 470 8090) can let you know what is going on in your local area.

- **Fill your diary:** It can feel less lonely if you plan the week and put things in your diary to look forward to each day, such as a walk in the park or going to a local coffee shop, library, sports centre, cinema or museum. Try setting yourself targets for the week and building up slowly.

- **Get out and about:** Do not wait for people to come and see you: go and see them. One advantage of being older is that public transport is better value for the elderly. Local bus travel is free for older people across England. The age at which you can apply for your free bus pass depends on when you were born and where you live. Contact your local council for how to apply. There may also be community transport schemes operating in your area. Ask in your local library or GP practice or contact The Royal Voluntary Service (https://www.royalvoluntaryservice.org.uk/our-services/getting-out-and-about/community-transport/)

- **Help others:** Use the knowledge and experience you have gained over a lifetime to give something back to your community. You will get lots back in return, such as new skills and confidence, and you'll hopefully make some new friends too. You could help out at a local charity shop or hospital or become a reading buddy and help out a local school.

- **Join the University of the Third Age:** The University of the Third Age (U3A) operates in many areas and offers older people the chance to learn or do something new. Run by volunteers, the U3A has no exams. Instead, it gives you the chance to do, play or learn something you have never done before, or something you have not considered since you were at school. U3A is also a great place to meet people and make new friends. To find your nearest U3A visit (https://www.u3a.org.uk/find). (Taken from Loneliness in older people www.nhs.uk/)

Try setting targets with the older person you care for. This can be done weekly and then build up the activities slowly at a pace that suits the older person and you if you are doing some activities together.

What the older person would like to do this week	Add to the older person's diary when arrangements have been made.	Achieved?

Although loneliness and depression are distinct experiences, the two are linked and one can lead to the other.

Depression

Depression is a common mental health problem. It is reported to affect one in ten older adults over the age of 75, whilst a third may have symptoms of low mood. A low mood that does not lift may be a sign of depression. However, depression is not just about low mood; the older person may experience the following:

Thoughts and feelings
o loss of interest in life, including things they previously enjoyed,
o feeling helpless or hopeless,
o worrying or feeling anxious,
o feeling irritable or angry,
o difficultly concentrating,
o problems with memory,
o feeling bored or restless or being irritable with other people or avoiding them,
o being tearful,
o thoughts of self-harm or wanting to end their life,
o feeling they have let themselves or others down,
o feeling guilty.

Physical symptoms and behavioural changes

Older people with depression usually have more physical symptoms. These include:
o trouble sleeping or sleeping too much,
o over or under eating or loss of appetite,
o having no energy and feeling tired for no reason,
o loss of libido,
o dizziness and faintness,
o constipation. (Taken from *Dealing with depression –* Independent Age.)

Depression and Dementia

It can be difficult to distinguish between depression and dementia because they share some of the same symptoms listed above. Many older people who experience memory problems and difficulty concentrating often worry they may have dementia, but the problem may be that they are depressed. The shared symptoms can also make it harder to diagnose depression if the older person already has dementia.

If the older person is experiencing any of the symptoms listed above and you think they may be depressed, before seeing a GP, if they can visit, ask them to complete the Patient Health Questionnaire below. This will give the GP a good starting point in assessing if they are depressed, and the severity of the older person's condition.

If you think the older person you are caring for may have dementia speak to a GP. Also, a good resource for help and advice is the Alzheimer's Society (www.alzheimers.org.uk).

Patient Health Questionnaire (PHQ-9)	
Over the last two weeks, how often have you been bothered by any of the following problems?	
Little interest or pleasure in doing things?	o Not at all o Several days o More than half the days o Nearly every day
Feeling down, depressed, or hopeless?	o Not at all o Several days o More than half the days o Nearly everyday
Trouble falling or staying asleep, or sleeping too much?	o Not at all o Several days o More than half the days o Nearly everyday
Feeling tired or having little energy?	o Not at all o Several days

	○ More than half the days
	○ Nearly everyday
Poor appetite or overeating?	○ Not at all
	○ Several days
	○ More than half the days
	○ Nearly everyday
Feeling bad about yourself – or that you are a failure or have let yourself or your family down?	○ Not at all
	○ Several days
	○ More than half the days
	○ Nearly everyday
Trouble concentrating on things, such as reading the newspaper or watching television?	○ Not at all
	○ Several days
	○ More than half the days
	○ Nearly everyday
Moving or speaking so slowly that other people could have noticed? Or the opposite – being so fidgety or restless that you have been moving around a lot more than usual?	○ Not at all
	○ Several days
	○ More than half the days
	○ Nearly everyday
Thoughts that you would be better off dead, or of hurting yourself in some way?	○ Not at all
	○ Several days
	○ More than half the days
	○ Nearly everyday
Score 0 for not at all, up to 3 for nearly every day **Total /27**	
Depression Severity: 0-4 None, 5-9 mild, 10-14 moderate, 15-19 moderately severe, 20-27 severe	

Recent research highlighted that depressive symptoms are common in later life and contribute to the functional and cognitive decline in older people. (https://bjgp.org/content/early/2019/02/11/bjgp19X701297) The research found that despite older people expressing preferences for talking therapies, they are less likely to be referred than younger adults, particularly when aged 80 years or over. The research concludes that mental ill health needs to be a greater concern in the care of older adults and given the same level of importance as physical health. This includes access to psychological services that meet the older person's needs, e.g. cognitive behavioural therapy, etc.

In meeting the needs of Vera (the case study in box 1) talking therapies may have helped her to cope with the ageing process and whatever other thoughts and feelings she was experiencing, which contributed to her low mood and despair.

If you think the older person you are caring for would benefit from therapy, e.g. cognitive behavioural therapy or other talking therapies, you can refer them directly to an NHS psychological therapies service https://www.nhs.uk/service-search/find-a-psychological-therapies-service/ or speak to a GP.

Chapter 6

"Caring about others, running the risk of feeling, and leaving an impact on people, brings happiness." – *Harold Kushner, Rabbi.*

Many people do not recognise themselves as 'carers'. They see themselves as a husband, wife, son, daughter or friend looking after someone they love. But if you provide regular, unpaid help and support to a loved one who is struggling to cope alone then you are a carer.

Caring for a partner, relative or friend can be very rewarding and bring you closer together, but it can also be emotionally draining and you may feel isolated and alone; although you are far from alone because there are an estimated 6.5 million carers in the UK. As a carer, you may be providing help and support 24 hours, 7 days a week if the person you are supporting lives with you. If you live separately, you might spend a few hours a day with them, or pop in once a week.

What carers do

A carer helps someone cope with day to day living. Depending on their condition, the person you care for might require more help on some days than on others. All circumstances are different, but a carer might help with any of the following:

- personal care: washing, dressing, taking medication,
- household tasks: shopping, cleaning, cooking, laundry,
- financial matters: dealing with bills, writing letters,
- supervision: watching over someone who cannot be left alone,
- travel assistance: getting out and about, going to appointments,
- emotional support: friendship, listening, and advice.

Many carers can all too easily get caught in a cycle of resentment and guilt: resentment that they feel their life is no longer their own and guilt for feeling like this. It is important to acknowledge these feelings and not to bottle them up. It is also important to make sure that you look after yourself, including thinking about your feelings.

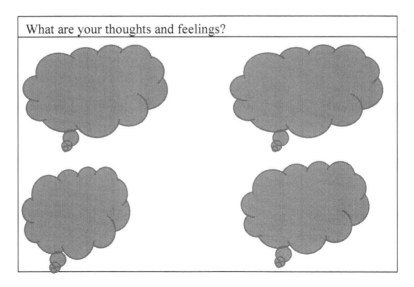

What are your thoughts and feelings?

Resentment: It is normal to feel resentful that your life is not perhaps how you imagined it to be. Perhaps your relationship with the person you care for has changed and you miss how it used to be. (This will be discussed more in chapter 7.) The person you are caring for may not always seem to appreciate what you are doing for them. You are bound to be affected by this.

Guilt: In your caring role, you may feel you should be doing more, or doing something better. This leads to feelings of guilt that you are not doing a good enough job. The person you care for may also feel guilty; they may feel they are being a 'burden' on you or they see the affect caring has on your life.

Acknowledge these feelings and try to understand that they are perfectly normal feelings. Talking to other carers about your feelings may help. It is important that you look after yourself and try to continue to do things you enjoy. The Carers UK Forum can offer help and support to you (https://www.carersuk.org/help-and-advice/get-support/carersuk-forum).

Help and Support for Carers

Recognising your role as a carer is an important step towards ensuring you get the right help and support, as follows:

- All carers are entitled to a free carer's assessment of their needs. This can be an important first step forward to finding support.
- Carers are protected by certain rights in the workplace.
- Being a carer can also bring particular financial

pressures, so it is essential to find out if you are eligible for support. (Taken from Carers and Caring, Which? Later Life Care).

The Carer's Assessment

If you care for someone, as described above, you can ask your local council to assess your needs to find out if you are eligible for support. This is known as a Carer's Assessment. A Carer's Assessment is free; to qualify you must be over 18 years of age and provide care for someone who is also over 18. It does not matter how much care you provide or what your situation is; if your life is affected by your caring responsibilities and you feel you need some support, then you should be offered a Carer's Assessment. To get a Carer's Assessment, contact your adult social care at your local council and request a Carer's Assessment. You can also speak to your GP and ask for a Carer's Assessment. A Carer's Assessment is different from a Needs Assessment (as described in chapter 1) because it looks at the carer's needs rather than the needs of the person you care for. You can ask both to be carried out at the same time, but you need to consider if you will be able to talk freely and honestly if the person you care for is present.

What does a Carer's Assessment involve?

At a convenient time for you, someone from your local council will usually come to your home and have a face-to-face meeting with you to discuss your needs. Some councils may do this over the phone or online. Assessments usually take about an hour.

There are three key questions that the local council will need to consider when making their decision:

1. Are your needs the result of you providing care to another person?
2. Does your caring role affect you?
3. Is there, or is there likely to be, a significant impact on your wellbeing?

If the answer to all three questions is yes, you may be eligible for help and support. The carer's assessment will also take into account these specific factors:

- The level of care you are willing and able to provide.
- Whether you are providing regular and substantial amounts of care.
- The impact on your life, such as on your work and leisure time.

Assessments usually take about an hour. You can have someone with you other than the person you care for.

How to prepare for a Carer's Assessment

You will need:

- your NHS number (if you have it),
- your GP's name, address and phone number,
- contact details for anyone coming to the assessment with you,
- the name, address, date of birth and NHS number of the person you care for (if you have it),
- your phone number and/or email address.

Before your Carer's Assessment, it is a good idea to think about your role as a carer and to be honest about the impact it has on your life. It may help to talk this through with a friend or relative, or to keep a diary for a week to write down the care you give and how this affects you and makes you feel.

During the assessment, you need to be honest and realistic about the amount of care you are realistically able to give or want to give. Try not to let feelings of guilt push you into providing more care for a loved one than you can cope with. This is not a time to be stoic and to put on a brave face. In a lot of cases, it is better if trained carers carry out certain tasks, e.g. personal care (washing and dressing) leaving you available for more social and emotional support, like trips out or having time to sit and have a cup of tea and a chat with the person you care for.

As suggested by *Which? Later Life Care*, think about the following before the assessment, make notes and take them to the assessment with you:

- Will you be able to talk freely if the person you care for is present?
- Do you want, or are you able, to carry on caring for your family member or friend?
- If you are prepared to continue, is there anything that could make your life easier?
- Without support, is there a risk that you might not be able to continue caring for your family member or friend?
- Do you have any physical or mental health problems, including stress or depression, that makes your role as a carer more difficult?
- Does being a carer affect your relationship with other people, including the person you are caring for and other family and friends?
- If you have a job, does being a carer cause any problems?
- Would you like more time to yourself so that you can sleep, take a break or enjoy some leisure activity? If

so, what would you like to do?
- Would you like to do some training, voluntary work or paid work? If so, what would you like to do?

```
Notes/What are the questions you want to ask
```

What happens after the assessment?

You will usually get the outcome of the assessment within a week. If you qualify for help from the council, it will agree to a care and support plan with you that sets out how it can help. If you are told you do not qualify for help and support from your council, you should be given a written decision explaining this. However, do ask the council for free advice on where within your community you can get some help and support.

If you disagree with the outcome of your Carer's Assessment, or how it was carried out, you can complain. Ask your council for its formal complaints procedure and how to complain about your Carer's Assessment.

If your council decides you have eligible needs, it may offer you support in a range of ways, such as:

Practical support for the person you look after

If you need a break from caring, you may be offered alternative care, such as:

- a sitting service, where someone can sit with the person you are looking after to take over your supervision role for a while,
- respite care for the person you are looking after; this may be a place in a day- care centre or a short time in a residential care home, which would enable you to have a holiday or take a break.

Practical support for you as the carer

As a carer, you might be offered support such as:

- gym membership and leisure classes to help relieve stress,
- taxi fares, if you do not drive, to help you get out and about,
- help with housework or gardening tasks,
- a carer's training session on lifting and handling techniques,
- computer training, and other courses, to help you get a job or to stay in your current one.

Some services will be provided directly by your council, others will be from other providers.

Financial support

If you spend a certain number of hours caring for someone, you may be entitled to certain benefits:

Carer's Allowance can be claimed if you provide care for someone for at least 35 hours a week (£67.60 a week: the rate in 2021/2022). You do not have to be related to, or live with, the person you care for.

Carer's Credit can be claimed if you provide care for someone for at least 20 hours a week and are unable to work because of your caring responsibilities, and therefore cannot make National Insurance contributions. Carer's Credit helps build your entitlement to the basic State Pension by making sure there are no gaps in your National Insurance contribution record.

Is council support for carers free?

If you are assessed as having eligible needs, your council has a legal duty to meet those needs. Some councils offer help and support to carers free of charge, following the Carer's Assessment, but some councils will carry out a financial assessment to find out if you will need to contribute towards the help that is offered to you.

If a financial assessment is carried out, it will be similar to the type of means test described in chapter 2, which determines if an older person is eligible for help towards funding their care.

Box 6 – Case Study

Sonnie was the main carer for his father, who had Parkinson's disease and mild dementia. He was finding juggling his work commitments and caring for his father difficult. He requested a Carer's Assessment from his local council.

The social worker who carried out the assessment suggested that one thing Sonnie could do was to speak to his employer about flexible working. This could help Sonnie to find a working pattern that suits his caring role, and it may give him more time to himself to do the things he enjoyed. Sonnie worked full-time and spent most of his evenings and weekends shopping and caring for his father; this left him with very little time to spend with his family. His employer suggested he try working compressed hours: that is, he works all his normal hours over fewer days. Sonnie decided to work his hours over

---

four days, which would give him a free day in the week.

The outcome of the Carer's Assessment outlined that Sonnie was eligible for support from his local council. The support offered for his father was two days a week at a day centre and also two weeks a year respite in a residential care home.

Between the change in his working pattern and the help offered by the council, this gave Sonnie much more time to be with his family. It also meant that he could have a holiday with his family knowing that his father would be well cared for in a residential home. His father was also enjoying going to the day centre and socialising two days a week.

Sonnie did have to make a small financial contribution for the two weeks of respite care.

The following checklist is a useful tool to help you get the support and information you need as a carer.

Checklist for carers

Your wellbeing

- ○ get a carer's assessment from your local council,
- ○ register as a carer with your GP,
- ○ make time for yourself and your interests as often as you can,
- ○ take a break from caring – there are ways to arrange respite care.

Your money

- ○ apply for Carer's Allowance,
- ○ use Age UK's benefits calculator to check if there are any other benefits you could be claiming for the

person you care for.

Your work

- ○ tell your employer about your caring responsibilities,

- ○ think about asking for flexible working.

For the person that you are caring for

- ○ make sure they have a care Needs Assessment from the local council,

- ○ help them complete a benefits check,

- ○ consider if any home adaptions would make their life easier,

- ○ it may be useful to think about future care needs, their preferences, Power of Attorney and whether their Will is up to date.

Caring can sometimes feel lonely, and it is okay to admit it is all getting a bit much. There are people you can talk to for advice, support or just a listening ear:

- ○ your local Age UK,

- ○ a relevant charity, e.g. Parkinson's UK, Alzheimer's Society, MS Society,

- ○ your doctor or other healthcare providers,

- ○ a carer's group, e.g. Carers UK,

- ○ online forums,

- ○ memory cafes.

The checklist has been taken from Age UK. For more information on each item, go to www.ageuk.org.uk/carerschecklist.

Chapter 7

"Be determined to handle any challenge in a way that will make you grow." – *Les Brown.*

We all will experience grief and loss at some time in our lives. There is no one way of grieving; everyone copes with loss or bereavement differently. Models of grief and loss outline the experiences that people go through following a significant loss. Some writers propose that people progress through recognisable stages, whilst other writers suggest that the response to loss is more fluid in nature.

The most common and intense experience of loss is due to bereavement, i.e. someone important to you has died. However, the feeling of loss can also be experienced following a significant change in your life that was unwanted, e.g. diagnosed with an illness or due to an acquired disability.

The stages model of grief proposed by Kuber-Ross (1969) remains a popular model when considering and attempting to understand grief. Kuber-Ross suggests there are five stages of grief:

Denial: On first hearing of a person's death there may be disbelief, *"This isn't happening." "It's not true!"* The person may temporarily hang on to the hope that the deceased person will walk in as normal. During this stage, numbness and shock may also be felt.

Anger: In the second stage, the individual recognises that denial cannot continue and the strength of the pain results in anger. This anger can be directed at anyone, and sometimes involves envy, *"Why me and not them ... they deserve it more than me!"* Anger can also be directed at the deceased person because the individual blames them.

Bargaining: Some people try to negotiate with a higher power, such as God, asking for another chance to go back to how things were before: bargaining that if they were given another chance they would do things differently, *"Please give me another chance, I will be a better person from now on!"*

Depression: Once the person starts to absorb the full truth, they may become very sad and withdrawn. They can feel a sense of great loneliness and hopelessness and are often tearful and emotional. During this stage, they may neglect routine activities, such as caring for themself because they often state, *"I just don't have the energy to get out of bed."*

Acceptance: During this stage, the person starts to come to terms with their loss. They accept that they will have to continue without their loved one but that the loved one will not be forgotten.

Whilst this model describes some emotions and behaviours that may be experienced by the bereaved, it is important to say that everyone deals with bereavement differently. After a death, thoughts and feelings can be chaotic and overwhelming, and it may be difficult to put into words exactly how you are feeling.

Grief does not just affect you emotionally; it can also produce physical symptoms. Like other forms of stress, bereavement can weaken our immune system, making us more susceptible to illness. People often think of stress and anxiety as mental health problems, but they can also produce physical symptoms.

You might experience:
- exhaustion,
- loss of appetite or comfort eating,
- panic attacks,
- aches and pains, such as chest pain and headaches,
- shaking,
- breathing problems,
- disturbed sleep at night or nightmares.

(Taken from Coping with bereavement produced by Independent Age www.independentage.org)

The grieving process is also relevant to situations where no one has died but the person experiences a significant loss. For example, Vera, in the case study in chapter 1 (box 1) was trying to come to terms with the loss of her mobility and loss of her independence. She was finding this difficult and it appeared she was showing signs that she was going through some of the stages of the grief process. She showed denial by refusing the help and support that was arranged for her and showed anger towards her family. She was also depressed – which we have already discussed in chapter 5 that talking therapies may have been of benefit.

When the older person being cared for has dementia, many family and friends of that person report that they go through a grieving process for the person they once knew.

What is dementia?

Dementia is a syndrome (a group of related symptoms)

associated with an ongoing decline of brain functioning. This may include problems with:

- memory loss,
- thinking speed,
- mental sharpness and quickness,
- language,
- understanding,
- judgement,
- mood,
- movement,
- difficulties carrying out daily activities.

According to NHS.UK (www.nhs.uk/) there are many different causes of dementia. People often get confused about the difference between Alzheimer's disease and dementia. Alzheimer's disease is a type of dementia and together with vascular dementia makes up the vast majority of cases.

People with dementia can become apathetic or uninterested in their usual activities, or may have problems controlling their emotions. They can become tearful for no apparent reason, or angry and lash out at loved ones. Social situations may also become challenging and they may lose interest in socialising.

Families often report that the person with dementia has become less understanding of them and other people, and they have lost the ability to show compassion. Due to the decline in brain function, as described above, and often the personality change in the person affected, many families grieve for their loved one whilst they are still living. They grieve for the person that was: for the person that they feel they have lost.

Some families feel that their loved one has 'died' socially before they die physically. They often report that the person is an 'empty shell' of the person they once were. When physical death does come, families often report to feeling relieved, because they have already grieved for the person they loved.

Box 7 – Case Study

Betty's family were concerned that she was getting increasingly forgetful and at times would forget who her family members were. After seeing her GP, who referred her to a specialist clinic, she was diagnosed with dementia.

Betty was still able to live at home with some help and support from her family and carers. At first, she was able to make her own decisions about what to buy at the local shops, and she was able to manage her finances, such as going to the Post Office and withdrawing cash from her account where her pension was paid in. Her family was able to offer some support with things like paying bills, etc.

However, Betty's condition quickly started to deteriorate. She was struggling to make decisions on some days and she was struggling with getting around the house and using the toilet. Her family were concerned and spoke to Betty's social worker. The social worker outlined The Mental Capacity Act, stating that it is designed to protect and empower people who may lack the mental capacity to make their own decisions. At this stage, Betty's family considered that Betty did have the mental capacity to make decisions about her future. They decided to have a family meeting, which included Betty, to decide what would be in Betty's best interests for the future.

During the family meeting, Betty was able to express what she wanted for the future. She stated that she wanted to stay in her own home for as long as possible but was prepared to go into a care home if she was no longer managing at home. Her family found it difficult to raise the issue of finances with Betty but felt it was important to do this to plan ahead. Betty agreed to see a solicitor and make a Will.

The solicitor suggested to Betty and her family representatives that as well as making a Will, Betty should consider setting up a Lasting Power of Attorney. This would give someone she trusts the right to make decisions about her money and welfare on her behalf, because this may be needed in the future as Betty's mental capacity declined. Betty agreed this was a good idea and nominated her eldest daughter, Josephine and her son, William. The solicitor asked Betty the relevant questions and considered she had the capacity, on that day, to make such a decision. He suggested that due to the nature of Betty's condition, and her recent deterioration, she should give Josephine and William, as her joint attorneys, the right to make decisions about her financial affairs as well as about her health and welfare, when that was needed in the future.

Although Betty's family found this a difficult thing to do, they still encouraged Betty to make decisions as and when she was able by allowing her more time or asking her things in the morning when she was more alert. On some days she was able to make decisions on others she was not.

As Betty's dementia progressed, she became unable to communicate with her family rationally and unable to care for herself at home, even with extensive support from her family and carers. Most members, but not all, of Betty's family thought the best option was to look for a care home that could meet Betty's needs. As Josephine and William were Betty's advocates (as her attorneys) they discussed the options with their siblings, and it was agreed a residential care home was the best option for their mother.

The family felt anger that their mother had such a horrible disease. They felt guilty that she was in a care home rather than being looked after at home, even though deep down they realised they would not have been able to cope. They went through an array of emotions and continued to seek answers and alternative options. But eventually, seeing Betty's decline, they accepted that their mother was dying. They watched as she withdrew from social activities and became unable to communicate or recognise them.

When Betty died, they felt sadness but a sense of great relief that she was at peace.

Chapter 8

"A good laugh and a long sleep are the two best cures for anything." – *Irish proverb*.

The concept of wellbeing is becoming increasingly important in health and social care. The Care Act 2014 introduced the "wellbeing principle" putting the idea of wellbeing at the centre of social care and support. This means that local councils must promote wellbeing when carrying out care and support tasks and also include the wellbeing principle when carrying out assessments, such as Needs Assessments and Carers' Assessments. A sense of wellbeing as a means of improving mental health, and to help make you feel more positive and get the most out of life, is just as important for carers as it is for the older person being cared for.

What is wellbeing?
The Care Act 2014 defines wellbeing as relating to the following areas, with each one being equally important:
- personal dignity, e.g. being treated with respect,
- physical and mental health and emotional wellbeing,
- protection from abuse and neglect,
- control by the individual over day-to-day life (including over the care and support provided, and the way it is provided),

- participation in work, education, training or recreation,
- social and economic wellbeing,
- domestic, family and personal relationships,
- suitability of living accommodation,
- the individual's contribution to society.

Evidence suggests there are 5 steps you can take to improve your mental health and wellbeing. (https://www.nefconsulting.com/our-services/strategy-culture-change/wellbeing/) NHS England (www.nhs.uk/) suggests trying these things could help you feel more positive and be able to get the most from life.

Step 1: Connect with others

Good relationships are important for your mental wellbeing. They can:
- help you build a sense of belonging and self-worth,
- give you an opportunity to share positive experiences,
- provide emotional support and allow you to support others.

Do

- ✓ if possible, take time each day to be with your family, for example, try arranging a fixed time to eat dinner together

- ✓ arrange a day out with friends you have not seen for a while

- ✓ try switching off the TV to talk or play a game with your children, friends or family

- ✓ have lunch with a colleague

- ✓ visit a friend or family member who needs support or company

- ✓ volunteer at a local school, hospital or community group

- ✓ make the most of technology to stay in touch with friends and family. Get used to using things like FaceTime and Skype, because this is a very useful way of keeping in touch with family and friends

- ✓ Find out through your GP surgery or local library how to access community groups in your area, such as Men's Sheds (https://menssheds.org.uk/).

Step 2: Be physically active

Being active is not only great for your physical health and fitness, but evidence shows it can also improve your mental wellbeing by:

- raising your self-esteem,
- helping you to set goals or challenges and achieve them,
- causing chemical changes in your brain, which can help to positively change your mood.

Do
- ✓ find free activities in your community to help you get fit: walking groups, etc.

- ✓ if you have a disability or long-term health condition, speak to your GP about exercise on prescription

- ✓ your local leisure centre will have information on activities for all abilities. Swimming and aqua fit classes are both great ways to get started with exercise.

Step 3: Learn new skills

Research shows that learning new skills can improve your mental wellbeing by:
- boosting self-confidence and raising self-esteem,
- helping you to build a sense of purpose,
- helping you to connect with others.

Do
- ✓ try learning to cook something new

- ✓ try taking on a new responsibility at work, such as mentoring or acting as a buddy for new or junior staff members

- ✓ work on a DIY project, e.g. something around the home or garden that you have been meaning to do. Some large DIY

> stores have teaching sessions to help learn the necessary skills
>
> ✓ consider signing up for a course at the local college, such as learning a new language or something more practical, such as plumbing or cookery classes. BUT do not feel you need to take exams or qualifications if this is not what you want
>
> ✓ try taking up a new hobby that challenges you, e.g. learning to paint or taking up a new sport.

Step 4: Give to others

Research suggests that acts of giving and kindness can help your mental wellbeing by:

- creating positive feelings and a sense of reward,
- giving you a feeling of purpose and self-worth,
- helping you connect with other people.

> Do
>
> ✓ say thank you to someone for something they have done for you
>
> ✓ ask friends, family or colleagues how they are and *really* listen to their answer
>
> ✓ spend time with friends or relatives who need support or company
>
> ✓ offer to help someone you know with DIY or a work project
>
> ✓ volunteer in your community, such as helping at a school, hospital or care home.

Step 5: Pay attention to the present moment (mindfulness)

Paying more attention to the present can improve your mental wellbeing. This includes your thoughts and feelings, your body and the world around you.

Some people call this awareness "mindfulness". Mindfulness can help you enjoy life more and understand yourself better. It can positively change the way you feel about life and how you approach challenges.

Do

    ✓ be curious and take notice of how you are feeling and the things around you

    ✓ find the beauty in your environment

    ✓ notice the changing seasons

    ✓ enjoy the moment and live in the present and not the past.

(Taken from 5 steps to mental wellbeing – NHS www.nhs.uk/)

Following the 5 steps to mental wellbeing can improve how you feel as a carer by improving your mental health and wellbeing. Encouraging the person you care for to do the same, or do some of the steps together, will also improve their sense of wellbeing.